Happy reading?!
Happy golfing?!
Susan
Greene

Hello!

Jamie

Terry

Pavy

Jimmy

Jimmy's HONEYBEAR CHAMPIONSHIP

SWEETLY SPONSORED
BY

FRIENDLYBEE HONEY

JIMMY	-15	DAVE	-12
TERRY	-14	GRACIE	-12
PAVY	-14	BENNY	-12
JAMIE	-14	BRIANA	+ 3

swing into OPPOSITES

OPPOSITES with golf

by Susan Greene

Illustrations by Dagne Angersbach Klavins

Excel Publishing, LLC

Troy, Michigan

For Pavlos, a terrific "Chief Editor" and great friend!

S.G.

Thanks to all for your invaluable support.

D.A.K.

Text and illustrations copyright © 2003 Susan Greene

First Edition 2003
Published by Excel Publishing

Library of Congress Catalog Card Number: 2002094890

International Standard Book Number: 0-9651100-4-4

Book design by Joanne Hack

Printed in Singapore

10 9 8 7 6 5 4 3 2 1

This golf bag is **big**.

This golf bag is small.

Some golfers are short,

and others quite tall.

But regardless of equipment, shape or size,
Golf is fun and filled with surprise!

This
budding
golfer is young.

This seasoned golfer is 𝕺𝕷𝕯.

Some golfers play when it's hot.

Some golfers play when it's **cold**.

The enjoyment of golf
is for each to behold!

Terry's golf bag is **heavy**.

Jamie's golf bag is light.
Take the equipment you feel is right!

or tee it **high**,

You can tee the ball **low**,

Then take your stance, and let it fly!

Examine the layout of every hole
Before you put your ball in flight,
Because some holes dogleg to the

left,

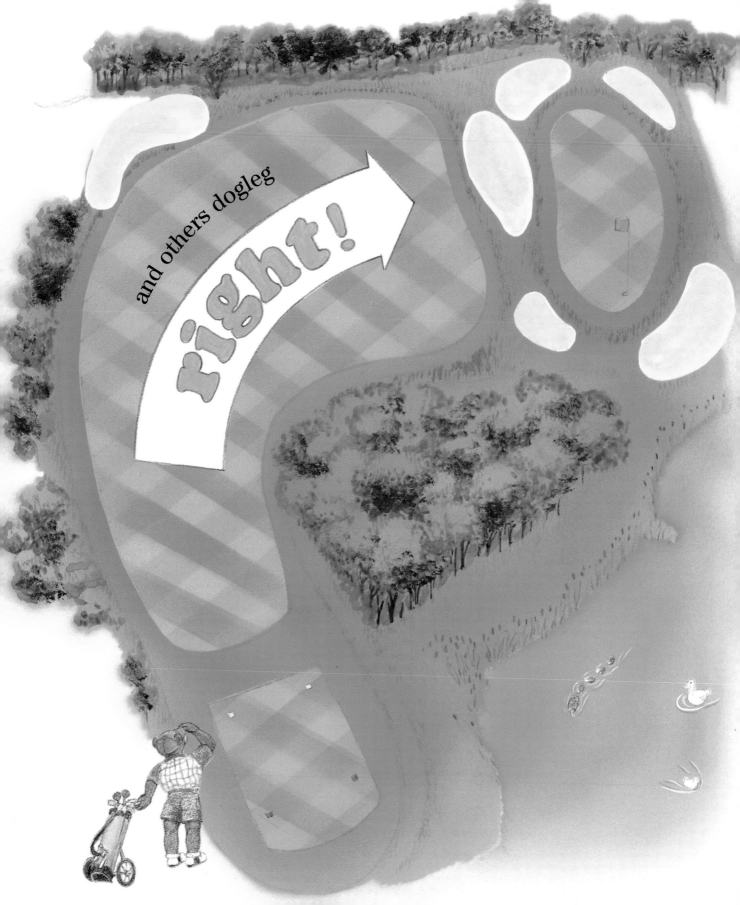

This flagstick is in the **front** of the green,

But as you play holes one through eighteen,

You may find a flagstick in the **back** of the green,

And just about anywhere in between!

To bring down your score!
That's one mindset you cannot ignore!

I'm having some tree trouble,
  as you can see.
Which shot will be right for me?

Should my ball fly *over* or *under* the tree?

The decision is for me to make.
I must decide what club to take!

Some
golf holes
are

narrow,

And others are

wide.

A wood or an iron?
It's time to decide!

Some golf shots make you *smile,*

While others make you *frown.*

Don't let a bad shot get you down.
Stay positive your entire round!

Your ball may not land
on **level** ground.

Uphill lies

and **downhill** lies are often found.

If you're a right-handed golfer, this rhyme is for you.
If you're a left-handed golfer, the opposite is true.

is determined by ball flight.
A **draw** soars from right to left and a **fade** from left to right.

On some holes you'll take many many many many many many many many strokes,

and others just a few.
few
few

Have some fun
with either result,
and start each
hole anew!

Some golfers tee it up
as early as
sunrise!

Playing all day,

until **sunset**, comes as no surprise!

This golf hole is 1 0

and this hole is short.

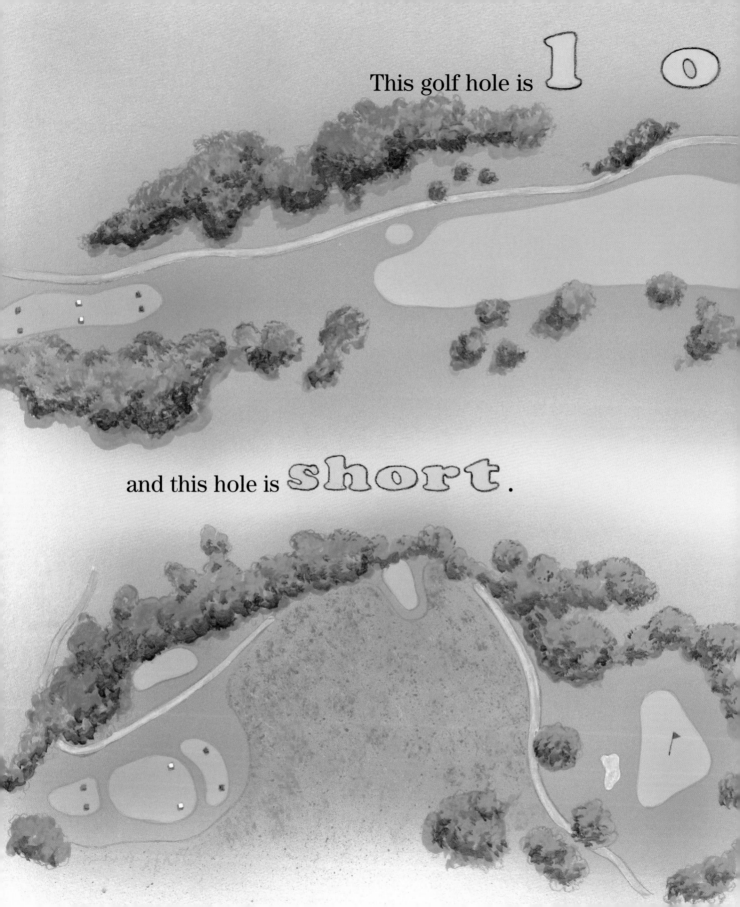

n g,

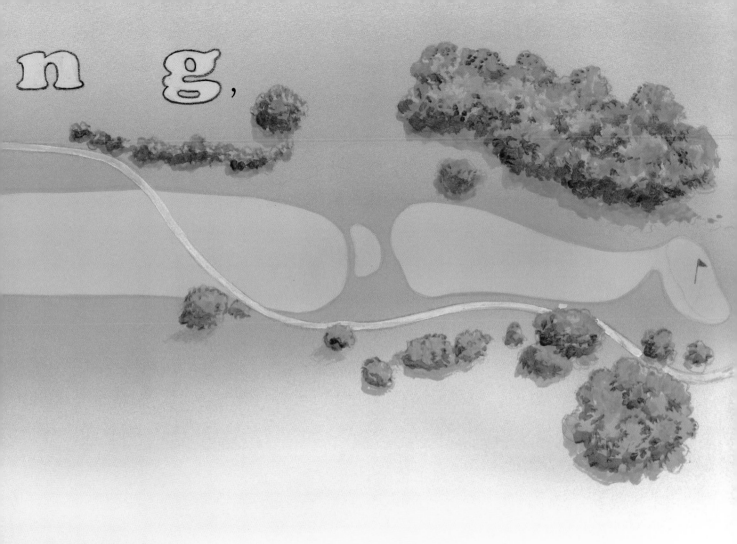

Each hole being different is part of the sport!

Jimmy is headed to the practice area with a **full** basket in hand,

To practice all shots, including those from the sand.

He'll hit each golf ball, one by one,

and empty his basket for improvement and fun!

Learning about opposites is so much fun!
Let's review them one by one!

1. What is the opposite of **big**?

2. What is the opposite of **tall**?

3. What is the opposite of **young**?

4. What is the opposite of **hot**?

5. What is the opposite of **heavy**?

6. What is the opposite of **low**?

7. What is the opposite of **left**?

8. What is the opposite of **front**?

9. What is the opposite of **positive**?

10 What is the opposite of **over**?

11 What is the opposite of **narrow**?

12 What is the opposite of **smile**?

13 What is the opposite of **uphill**?

14 What is the opposite of **draw**?

15 What is the opposite of **many**?

16 What is the opposite of **sunrise**?

17 What is the opposite of **long**?

18 What is the opposite of **empty**?

Good-bye!

Terry

Pavy

Jamie

Jimmy